Remember Me
When This You See

Compiled by LILLIAN MORRISON

Illustrated by MARJO~~~~

Authorized A

SCHOLASTIC BOOK SERVICES

Published by Scholastic Book Services, a division
of Scholastic Magazines, Inc., New York, N.Y.

For Adeline

Text Copyright © 1961 by Lillian Morrison. Illustrations copyright © 1961 by Marjorie Bauernschmidt. Copyright © 1964 by Scholastic Magazines, Inc. This abridged edition is published by Scholastic Book Services, a division of Scholastic Magazines, Inc., by arrangement with Thomas Y. Crowell Company and the author.

3rd printing   December 1966

Printed in the U.S.A.

Contents

Autograph writing is rather tough;
Here's my name and that's enough.

I have only two words to say.
I hope you will not cry,
And those two words that I will say
Are "Hi" and " 'Bye."

I 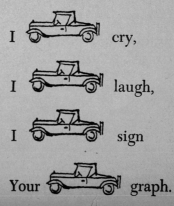 cry,

I laugh,

I sign

Your graph.

I'm a pilot without a plane
Who just dropped down to sign his name.

Roses are red,
Lilies are white;
Here is my autograph
To prove I can write.

I'm a square from Delaware
Just come to town to see the Fair.

When the name that I write here is dim on the page,
And the leaves of your album are yellow with age,
Still think of me kindly, and do not forget
That, wherever I am, I remember you yet.

What! Write in your book!
Where the learned may look!
Where the critic might spy!
No! Never! Not I!

My pen is poor,
My ink is gray,
When you see this
Don't faint away.

I pity the robber,
I pity the thief,
I pity the one
That steals this leaf.

My ink is pale,
My pen is frail,
My hand shakes like
A puppy dog's tail.

Janice Johnson is my name
And with this pen I write the same.
The grass is green, the rose is red;
Remember me when I am dead.

The owner of this book has asked
A word or two of me,
But being in a generous mood
I've written twenty-three.

(Count, please.)

I looked your album through and through
From one end to the other.
I find that you have many friends
And I will be another.

I'm the clown
Who came to town
And signed your book
Upside down.

Just to make you angry,
Just to make you frown,
I'm writing in your album
Upside down.

2, 4, 6, 8

How the heck did you graduate?

Remember the fights,
Remember the fun,
Remember the homework
That never got done.

Some good books to read:
I Fell Over the Cliff, by Eileen Dover
Jump Over the Cliff, by Hugo Furst

Come out of your coma
And get your diploma.

Poor little Linda
Sitting on a fence,
Trying to get to high school
Without any sense.

Now I lay me down to rest,
I pray I pass tomorrow's test;
If I die before I wake,
That's one less test I'll have to take.

Roses are red,
Violets are blue,
Cornmeal is mushy
And so are you.

I jumped in the river
And started to drown,
But when I saw Judy
I couldn't go down.

The more I think about it,
The more I know it's true,
I never met a girl yet
Half as nice as you.

Pretty as a picture,
Fit to be hung.

$$\begin{array}{r} 2 \\ 2 \\ \hline 4 \end{array}\ \begin{array}{l} \text{young} \\ \text{go} \\ \text{boys} \end{array}$$

19

Roses are red,
Violets are blue,
The sidewalk is cracked
And so are you.

Don't go to London,
Don't go to France,
Stay here in Kansas,
And give the boys a chance.

I have a little rooster,
I put him on the fence,
He crowed and crowed for Margie
Because he had good sense.

I wish I were a grapefruit
And here's the reason why.—
When you came to eat me,
I'd squirt you in the eye.

When I was a little boy
I used to hunt the squirrels,
But now I am a great big boy
I'd rather hunt the girls.

Sailors like ships,
Babies like toys,
But all that Betty likes
Is boys, boys, boys.

Susie, Susie, you're a wonder,
And when you are old and gray,
We will all say, "Yes, by thunder,
She was some girl in her day."

There's music in a kettle,
There's music in a spout,
There's music in Joanna,
But you can't get it out.

As long as grapes grow on a vine
You'll always be a friend of mine.

In your ocean of friends, please count me
as a permanent wave.

When you read these words I've penned,
Think upon me as your friend.

There is White Rose tea,
There is Ceylon tea,
But there's no tea
Like loyalty.

When a feather shall weigh a pound,
When a fox shall chase a hound,
When the world shall come to an end,
Then I shall cease to be your friend.

When rocks and rills divide us
And you no more I see,
Just take a pen or pencil
And drop a line to me.

Yours till bacon strips.

Yours till cement walks.

Yours till ice screams.

Yours till the banana splits.

30 Yours till the dogwood barks.

WOOF!
WOOF!